ADVANTAGE Math

M000306517

1

Table of Contents

Table of Contents

CREDITS

Concept Development: Kent Publishing Services, Inc.
Written by: Dawn Purney
Editor: Carla Hamaguchi
Designer/Production: Moonhee Pak/Mary Gagné
Illustrator: Darcy Tom
Art Director: Tom Cochrane
Project Director: Carolea Williams

Introduction

The Advantage Math Series for grades K–2 offers instruction and practice for key skills in each math strand recommended by the National Council for Teachers of Mathematics (NCTM), including

- numeration and number theory
- operations
- geometry
- measurement
- patterns, functions, and algebra
- data analysis and probability
- problem solving

Take a look at all the advantages this math series offers . . .

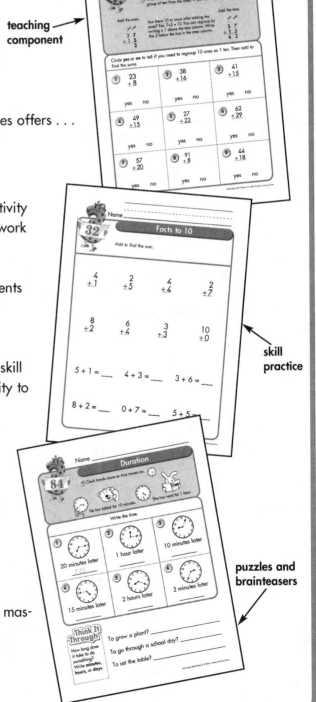

teaching component

skill practice

puzzles and brainteasers

Strong Skill Instruction

- The **teaching component** at the top of the activity pages provides the support children need to work through the book independently.

- Plenty of **skill practice** pages will ensure students master essential math computation skills they need to increase their math fluency.

- A **problem-solving strand** is woven between skill practice pages to offer students an opportunity to practice critical thinking skills.

Motivational Format

- The "Think It Through" feature provides **fun puzzles** and **brainteasers.**

- The "Get Ahead" feature helps students practice basic concepts in a fun way. Many of these activities focus on **mental math** and mastery of **basic facts.**

- The number **character mascot** adds a fun element to each activity page.

Introduction

Assessment

- In grades K–1, the "Put It All Together" pages provide **problem-solving challenges** and **mixed-skill review** of the concepts highlighted in that unit.

- In grades 1–2, the "Take a Test Drive" pages provide practice using a **test-taking** format such as the one included in national standardized and proficiency tests.

- The **tracking sheet** at the back of each book provides a motivational tool for children to use as they work their way from activity 1 to 100.

Answer Key

- Each page, with the answers completed, is reproduced in a miniature format at the back of the books to make **checking answers quick and easy.**

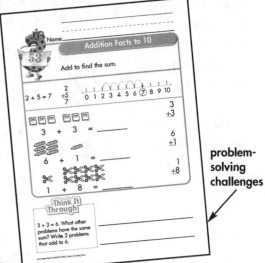

problem-solving challenges

skill review and test-taking practice

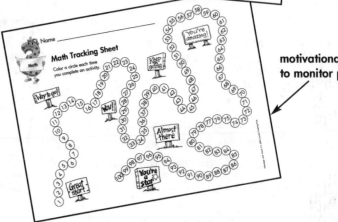

motivational way to monitor progress

Name _____

Write Numerals 0–4

★ There are 2 eggs in the nest.

2 2 2 2

Count the eggs. Trace the number. Then write it on your own.

0

1

2

3

4

Write Numerals 0–4

Count the birds. Write the number.

___ ____ ___	___ ____ ___	___ ____ ___
___ ____ ___	___ ____ ___	___ ____ ___
___ ____ ___	___ ____ ___	___ ____ ___

Name _____

Number Words to Five

Count the apples. Write the number. Trace the word.
Then write it on your own.

🍎	_____	one
🍎🍎	_____	two
🍎🍎🍎	_____	three
🍎🍎🍎🍎	_____	four
🍎🍎🍎🍎🍎	_____	five

Get Ahead ➤
Look around.
Count what
you see.

How many are on the ?

Number Words to Ten

8

Count the balls. Write the number. Trace the word. Then write it on your own.

six

seven

eight

nine

ten

Think It Through

Unscramble the number words. Write them on another sheet of paper.

ixs   higet   ereht

          neo

einn   net   rofu

    wot   vief   neves

Name _____

Ordinals

Look at the order. Mark the number.

Circle the first. Underline the third.

Circle the fourth. Underline the fifth.

Circle the second. Underline the third.

Name _____

Ordinals

Draw a line to match the order word to the correct elephant.

third

first

seventh

second

fifth

fourth

sixth

eighth

Look at the key. Color the balls.

Key to colors:
first = blue
second = red
fourth = yellow
seventh = purple
ninth = orange
tenth = green

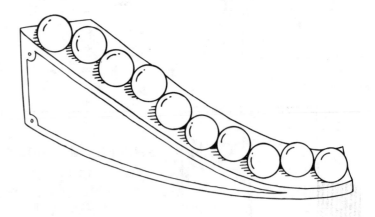

Place Value

★ 13 stands for 1 ten and 3 ones.   ★ 24 stands for 2 tens and 4 ones.

1 ten + 3 ones = 13   2 tens + 4 ones = 24

Write how many tens and ones. Then write how many in all.

____ ____ = _____
tens   ones

____ ____ = _____
tens   ones

____ ____ = _____
tens   ones

____ ____ = _____
tens   ones

____ ____ = _____
tens   ones

____ ____ = _____
tens   ones

Place Value

Circle groups of ten. Write how many tens and ones.
Then write how many in all.

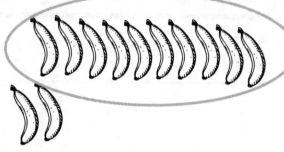

_____ _____ = _____
tens   ones

_____ _____ = _____
tens   ones

_____ _____ = _____
tens   ones

_____ _____ = _____
tens   ones

_____ _____ = _____
tens   ones

_____ _____ = _____
tens   ones

Count to Twenty

What comes after the number 10? Write each number.

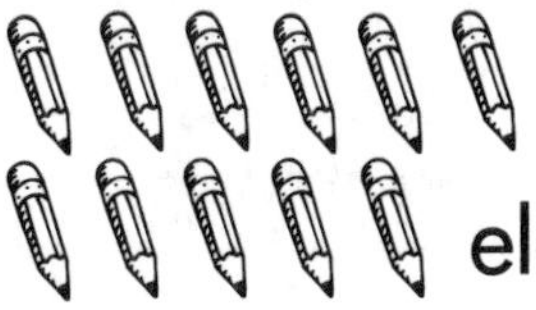

eleven - - - - - - _____

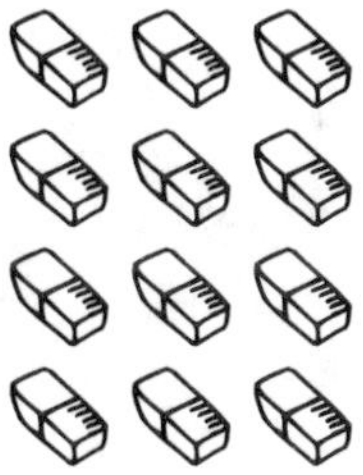

twelve - - - - - - _____

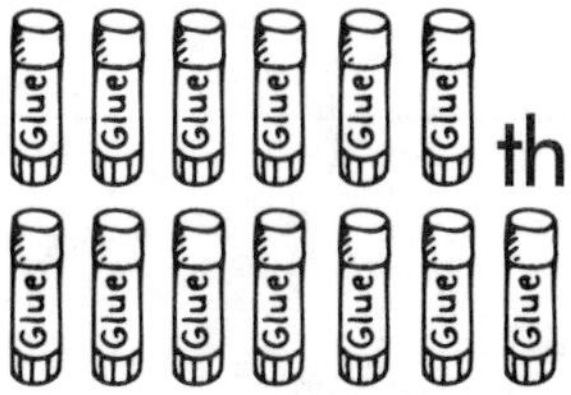

thirteen - - - - - - _____

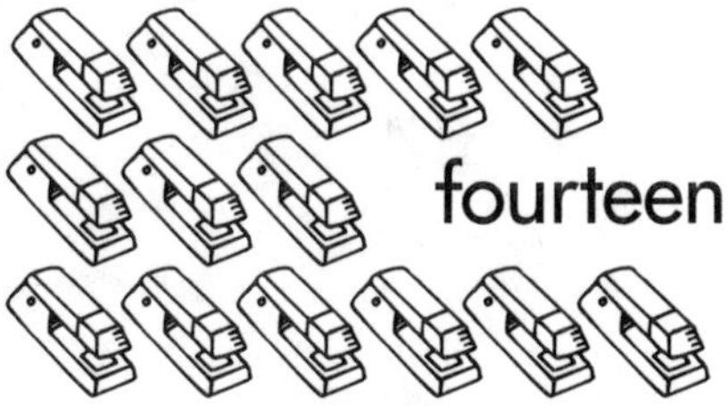

fourteen - - - - - - _____

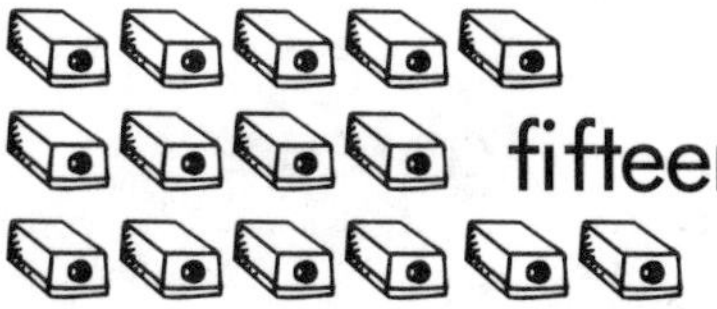

fifteen - - - - - - _____

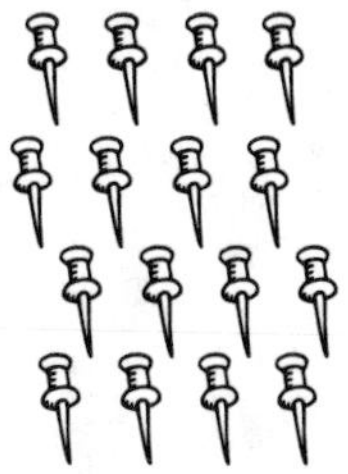

sixteen - - - - - - _____

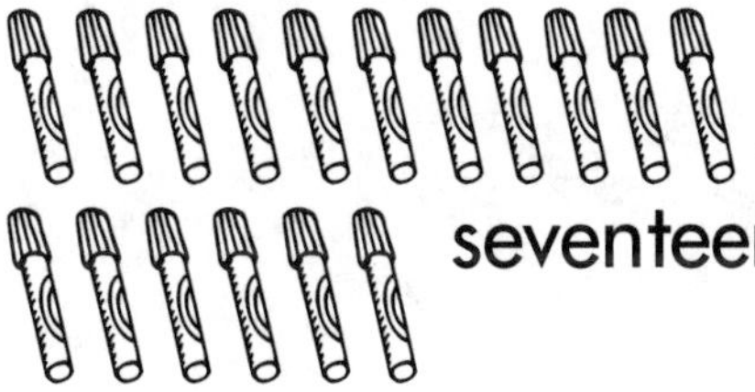

seventeen - - - - - - _____

eighteen - - - - - - _____

nineteen - - - - - - _____

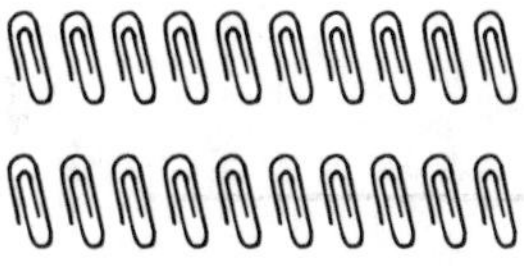

twenty - - - - - - _____

Count to Twenty

Draw a line to match the picture, number, and word.

12   twelve

17   twenty

20   fourteen

14   seventeen

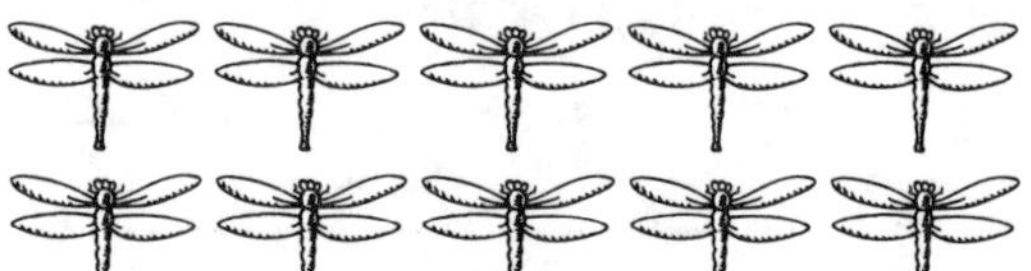

10   nineteen

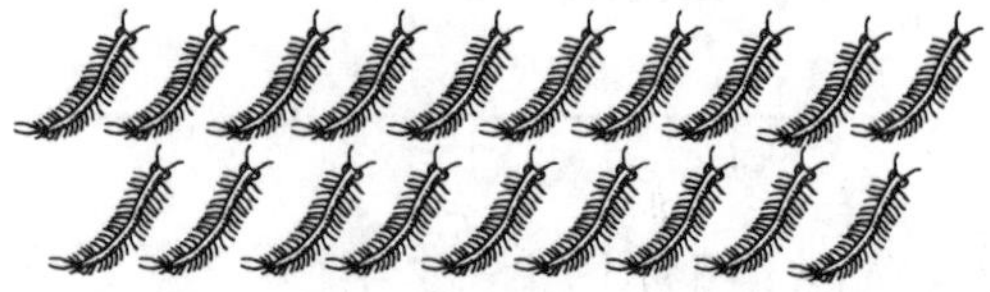

15   fifteen

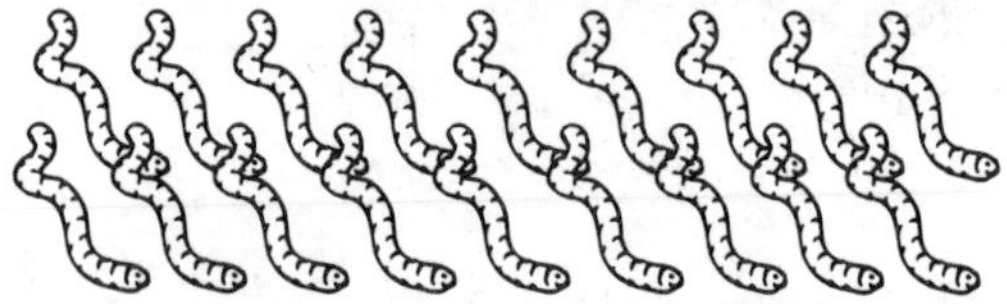

19   ten

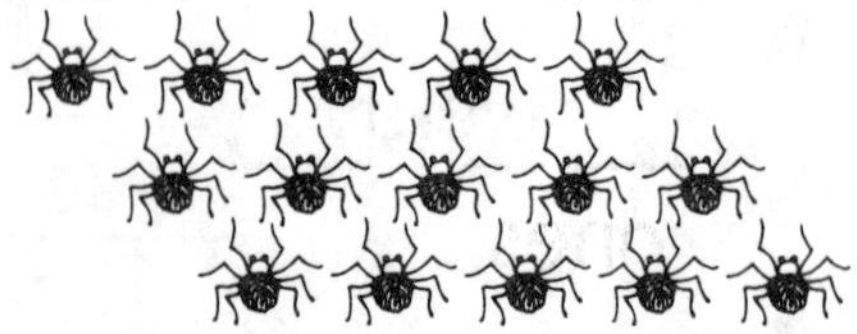

18   eighteen

Name _____

Count to One Hundred

Count the tens and ones. Write how many tens and ones.
Then write how many in all.

____   ____ = _____
tens   ones

____   ____ = _____
tens   ones

____   ____ = _____
tens   ones

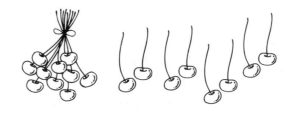

____   ____ = _____
tens   ones

____   ____ = _____
tens   ones

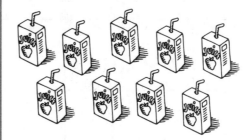

____   ____ = _____
tens   ones

Count to One Hundred

Follow the pattern to complete the chart.

1				5				9	
11	12				16				20
	22					27			30
31				35			38		
41		43			46			49	50
	52					57			60
61			64				68		70
		73		75				79	
81			84			87			90
				95					100

Order Numbers

Write the number that comes **next.**

12, 13, 14, _____   23, 24, 25, _____

79, 80, 81, _____   45, 46, 47, _____

37, 38, 39, _____   88, 89, 90, _____

64, 65, 66, _____   97, 98, 99, _____

8, 9, 10, _____   56, 57, 58, _____

30, 31, 32, _____   41, 42, 43, _____

Name _____

Order Numbers

Write the number that comes **before**.

___ 22   ___ 57   ___ 9

___ 74   ___ 81   ___ 40

___ 49   ___ 60   ___ 38

___ 33   ___ 65   ___ 26

Think It Through

Which is first? Which is second? Which is third? The crayons are red, blue, and yellow. Use the clues to color the crayons the correct color.

1. The red crayon is to the left of the yellow crayon.

2. Neither the blue crayon nor the red crayon is in the middle.

Skip Counting

It's fun to make a pattern by skip counting.

Show how the frog counts by 2's all the way to 12.

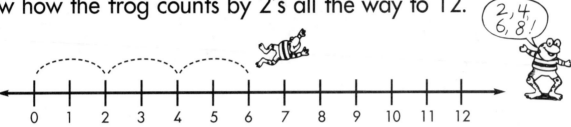

Show how the frog counts by 3's all the way to 12.

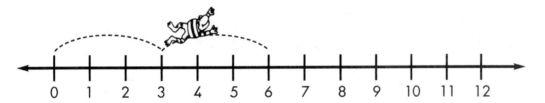

Show how the frog counts by 4's all the way to 12.

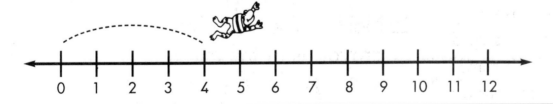

Show how the frog counts by 5's all the way to 15.

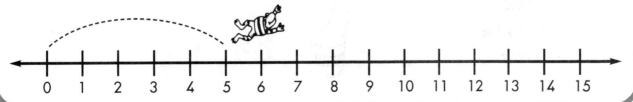

Skip Counting

Count the legs. Write how many on each line.

Skip count by the number given. Use the pictures above to help you.

by 2 __2__ __4__ _____

by 3 _____

Name _____

Facts to 5

Add to find the sum. 2 + 3 = 5

Count on from 2. 2, 3, 4, 5.

$$\begin{array}{r} 2 \\ +3 \\ \hline 5 \end{array}$$

2 + 3 = _5_

$$\begin{array}{r} 1 \\ +2 \\ \hline \end{array}$$

1 + 2 = ___

$$\begin{array}{r} 4 \\ +1 \\ \hline \end{array}$$

4 + 1 = ___

$$\begin{array}{r} 5 \\ +0 \\ \hline \end{array}$$

5 + 0 = ___

$$\begin{array}{r} 2 \\ +2 \\ \hline \end{array}$$

2 + 2 = ___

$$\begin{array}{r} 3 \\ +2 \\ \hline \end{array}$$

3 + 2 = ___

28

Facts to 5

Complete the picture. Add to find the sum.

○ ○ ○   0
                        + 3

0 + 3 = ___

△ △ △ △   4
                        + 1

4 + 1 = ___

☐   1
                        + 3

1 + 3 = ___

○ ○ ○ ○   4
                        + 3

4 + 3 = ___

◇ ◇   2
                        + 1

2 + 1 = ___

▭   1
                        + 4

1 + 4 = ___

31

Facts to 10

Complete the picture. Add to find the sum.

$$6 \\ +2$$

$$3 \\ +4$$

$$2 \\ +5$$

$$5 \\ +4$$

$$3 \\ +7$$

$$8 \\ +0$$

Think It Through

Count on to find the missing number.

$$1 + \boxed{} = 4$$

$$4 + \boxed{} = 6$$

$$5 + \boxed{} = 10$$

1 plus 2, 3, 4 !

Name _____

Add to find the sum.

$$\begin{array}{r} 4 \\ +1 \\ \hline \end{array} \qquad \begin{array}{r} 2 \\ +5 \\ \hline \end{array} \qquad \begin{array}{r} 4 \\ +4 \\ \hline \end{array} \qquad \begin{array}{r} 2 \\ +7 \\ \hline \end{array}$$

$$\begin{array}{r} 8 \\ +2 \\ \hline \end{array} \qquad \begin{array}{r} 6 \\ +4 \\ \hline \end{array} \qquad \begin{array}{r} 3 \\ +3 \\ \hline \end{array} \qquad \begin{array}{r} 10 \\ +0 \\ \hline \end{array}$$

$5 + 1 = \underline{} \qquad 4 + 3 = \underline{} \qquad 3 + 6 = \underline{}$

$8 + 2 = \underline{} \qquad 0 + 7 = \underline{} \qquad 5 + 5 = \underline{}$

33

Addition to Twenty

Complete the picture. Add to find the sum.

◇◇◇◇
◇◇◇◇
$\begin{array}{r} 8 \\ +3 \\ \hline \end{array}$

☆☆
$\begin{array}{r} 2 \\ +10 \\ \hline \end{array}$

△△△△
△△△
$\begin{array}{r} 7 \\ +6 \\ \hline \end{array}$

○○○○
○○○○
○
$\begin{array}{r} 9 \\ +4 \\ \hline \end{array}$

☆☆☆☆☆
$\begin{array}{r} 5 \\ +8 \\ \hline \end{array}$

○○○○○
○○○○○
$\begin{array}{r} 10 \\ +10 \\ \hline \end{array}$

□□□□
□□□
$\begin{array}{r} 7 \\ +7 \\ \hline \end{array}$

◇◇◇◇
◇◇◇
$\begin{array}{r} 7 \\ +8 \\ \hline \end{array}$

Addition to Twenty

Add to find the sum.

$$\begin{array}{r} 7 \\ +5 \\ \hline \end{array}$$ $$\begin{array}{r} 20 \\ +0 \\ \hline \end{array}$$ $$\begin{array}{r} 8 \\ +7 \\ \hline \end{array}$$ $$\begin{array}{r} 8 \\ +4 \\ \hline \end{array}$$

$$\begin{array}{r} 9 \\ +8 \\ \hline \end{array}$$ $$\begin{array}{r} 7 \\ +8 \\ \hline \end{array}$$ $$\begin{array}{r} 8 \\ +6 \\ \hline \end{array}$$ $$\begin{array}{r} 5 \\ +9 \\ \hline \end{array}$$

$$\begin{array}{r} 1 \\ +10 \\ \hline \end{array}$$ $$\begin{array}{r} 5 \\ +6 \\ \hline \end{array}$$ $$\begin{array}{r} 6 \\ +1 \\ \hline \end{array}$$ $$\begin{array}{r} 10 \\ +6 \\ \hline \end{array}$$

$4 + 7 = $ ___ $10 + 5 = $ ___ $8 + 8 = $ ___

Add 3 Numbers

Draw the picture. Add to find the sum.

$\begin{array}{r} 3 \\ 2 \\ +1 \\ \hline 6 \end{array}$	$\begin{array}{r} 1 \\ 2 \\ +1 \\ \hline \end{array}$
$\begin{array}{r} 6 \\ 3 \\ +0 \\ \hline \end{array}$	$\begin{array}{r} 2 \\ 4 \\ +1 \\ \hline \end{array}$
$5+1+2=$ ___	$3+4+2=$ ___
$4+5+1=$ ___	$2+0+7=$ ___

Name _____

Add 3 Numbers

Add to find the sum.

```
    0          3          4          6
    2          5          2          4
  + 1        + 1        + 2        + 5
  ———        ———        ———        ———
```

```
    6          8          5          7
    2          0          4          6
  + 3        + 1        + 3        + 3
  ———        ———        ———        ———
```

```
    1          2          3          5
    7          6          9          3
  + 4        + 0        + 2        + 6
  ———        ———        ———        ———
```

4 + 3 + 2 = ____   5 + 1 + 7 = ____

Add 1-Digit and 2-Digit Numbers

Complete the picture. Add to find the sum.

$$
\begin{array}{r} 1 \\ +10 \\ \hline \end{array}
$$

$$
\begin{array}{r} 11 \\ +3 \\ \hline \end{array}
$$

$$
\begin{array}{r} 4 \\ +14 \\ \hline \end{array}
$$

$$
\begin{array}{r} 9 \\ +7 \\ \hline \end{array}
$$

$$
\begin{array}{r} 15 \\ +5 \\ \hline \end{array}
$$

$$
\begin{array}{r} 6 \\ +10 \\ \hline \end{array}
$$

$$
\begin{array}{r} 12 \\ +6 \\ \hline \end{array}
$$

$$
\begin{array}{r} 10 \\ +8 \\ \hline \end{array}
$$

Name _____

Add 1-Digit and 2-Digit Numbers

Add to find the sum.

```
  12        16        13        11
 + 5       + 2       + 4       + 6
```

```
  19         7         5        14
 + 1       +13       +12       + 4
```

```
  15         0        11        17
 + 3       +20       + 8       + 3
```

```
  16         2         7        18
 + 4       +14       +10       + 1
```

Name _____

Take a Test Drive

Fill in the bubble to show the correct answer.

$\begin{array}{r} 4 \\ +1 \\ \hline \end{array}$	○ 4 ○ 5 ○ 6	$\begin{array}{r} 3 \\ +6 \\ \hline \end{array}$ ○ 7 ○ 8 ○ 9	$\begin{array}{r} 7 \\ +2 \\ \hline \end{array}$ ○ 7 ○ 8 ○ 9
$\begin{array}{r} 2 \\ +5 \\ \hline \end{array}$ ○ 6 ○ 7 ○ 8	$\begin{array}{r} 4 \\ +3 \\ \hline \end{array}$ ○ 5 ○ 6 ○ 7	$\begin{array}{r} 6 \\ +2 \\ \hline \end{array}$ ○ 6 ○ 7 ○ 8

Which picture matches the problem? $3 + 2 = 5$

○   ○   ○

Which problem matches the picture?

△ △ △ △ △
△ △ △ △ △   △ △ △

10 + 3   3 + 3   11 + 2
○   ○   ○

Name _____

Take a Test Drive

Fill in the bubble beside the correct answer.

7 +7	○ 14 ○ 15 ○ 16

12 +2	○ 13 ○ 14 ○ 15

9 +7	○ 11 ○ 16 ○ 17

5 +8	○ 11 ○ 12 ○ 13

12 +6	○ 14 ○ 18 ○ 19

5 +15	○ 10 ○ 18 ○ 20

3 2 +3	○ 5 ○ 6 ○ 8

1 5 +0	○ 5 ○ 6 ○ 7

Name _____

Facts to 5

Cross out shapes to show the number being subtracted.
Subtract to find the difference.

$$\begin{array}{r} 2 \\ -1 \\ \hline 1 \end{array}$$

2 − 1 = __1__

$$\begin{array}{r} 4 \\ -2 \\ \hline \end{array}$$

4 − 2 = ____

$$\begin{array}{r} 3 \\ -2 \\ \hline \end{array}$$

3 − 2 = ____

$$\begin{array}{r} 5 \\ -5 \\ \hline \end{array}$$

5 − 5 = ____

$$\begin{array}{r} 4 \\ -3 \\ \hline \end{array}$$

4 − 3 = ____

$$\begin{array}{r} 3 \\ -1 \\ \hline \end{array}$$

3 − 1 = ____

Name _____

Facts to 5

Cross out shapes to show the number being subtracted. Subtract to find the difference.

$$\begin{array}{r} 4 \\ -2 \\ \hline \end{array}$$

4−2=____

$$\begin{array}{r} 2 \\ -1 \\ \hline \end{array}$$

2−1=____

$$\begin{array}{r} 5 \\ -4 \\ \hline \end{array}$$

5−4=____

$$\begin{array}{r} 3 \\ -3 \\ \hline \end{array}$$

3−3=____

$$\begin{array}{r} 4 \\ -0 \\ \hline \end{array}$$

4−0=____

$$\begin{array}{r} 5 \\ -2 \\ \hline \end{array}$$

5−2=____

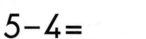

Name _____

Subtracting from 20 and Below

Draw the picture. Cross out the correct number. Subtract to find the difference.

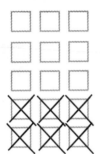

$$15$$
$$-6$$

$$19$$
$$-9$$

$$13$$
$$-7$$

$$15$$
$$-8$$

$20-10=$ _____

$18-9=$ _____

$16-8=$ _____

$13-5=$ _____

Subtracting from 20 and Below

Draw the picture. Cross out the correct number. Subtract to find the difference.

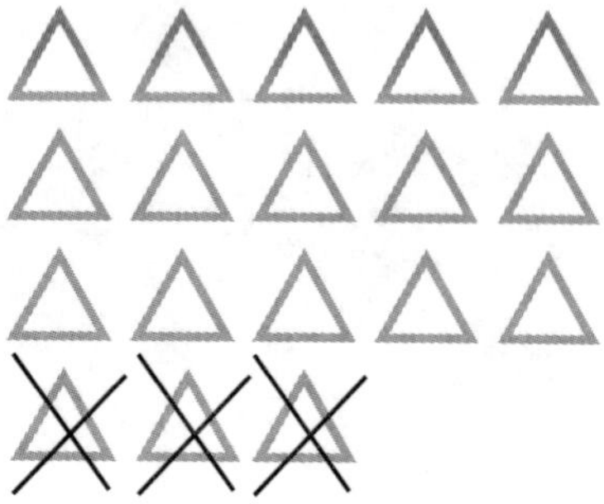

△ △ △ △ △   18
△ △ △ △ △   −3
△ △ △ △ △   ‾‾‾
X̷ X̷ X̷

16
−4
‾‾‾

14
−2
‾‾‾

19
−9
‾‾‾

17
−3
‾‾‾

12
−5
‾‾‾

20−6= _____   15−4= _____

Name _____

Subtracting from 20 and Below

Subtract to find the difference.

$$
\begin{array}{r} 17 \\ -8 \\ \hline \end{array}
\qquad
\begin{array}{r} 14 \\ -6 \\ \hline \end{array}
\qquad
\begin{array}{r} 11 \\ -5 \\ \hline \end{array}
\qquad
\begin{array}{r} 18 \\ -9 \\ \hline \end{array}
$$

$$
\begin{array}{r} 12 \\ -6 \\ \hline \end{array}
\qquad
\begin{array}{r} 15 \\ -9 \\ \hline \end{array}
\qquad
\begin{array}{r} 16 \\ -7 \\ \hline \end{array}
\qquad
\begin{array}{r} 14 \\ -5 \\ \hline \end{array}
$$

$19-9=$_____ $11-6=$_____ $17-8=$_____

$13-7=$_____ $15-5=$_____ $14-0=$_____

Advantage Math Grade 1 © 2004 Creative Teaching Press

Subtracting from 20 and Below

Subtract to find the difference.

$$
\begin{array}{r} 18 \\ -9 \\ \hline \end{array}
\qquad
\begin{array}{r} 16 \\ -5 \\ \hline \end{array}
\qquad
\begin{array}{r} 13 \\ -7 \\ \hline \end{array}
\qquad
\begin{array}{r} 10 \\ -7 \\ \hline \end{array}
$$

$$
\begin{array}{r} 17 \\ -3 \\ \hline \end{array}
\qquad
\begin{array}{r} 12 \\ -6 \\ \hline \end{array}
\qquad
\begin{array}{r} 15 \\ -8 \\ \hline \end{array}
\qquad
\begin{array}{r} 14 \\ -6 \\ \hline \end{array}
$$

Get Ahead

Read the story problem. Subtract to find the difference. Add to find the sum. Hint: A drawing may help you find the answer.

Ben had 12 🚗. He gave 4 🚗 to his friend Matt. On his birthday, Ben got 2 new 🚗.

How many 🚗 does Ben have now? _____

Advantage Math Grade 1 © 2004 Creative Teaching Press

Name _____

Put It All Together

Read the story problem. Then read the question. Cross out the correct number. Then subtract to find the difference.

---

4  eat.

2 🕊 fly away.

How many 🕊 are left?

$$\begin{array}{r} 4 \\ -2 \\ \hline \end{array}$$

---

9 🐟 swim.

5 🐟 swim away.

How many 🐟 are left?

$$\begin{array}{r} 9 \\ -5 \\ \hline \end{array}$$

---

7 🐰 sit.

1 🐰 hops away.

How many 🐰 are left?

$$\begin{array}{r} 7 \\ -1 \\ \hline \end{array}$$

---

12 🐛 dig.

8 🐛 stop.

How many 🐛 dig now?

$$\begin{array}{r} 12 \\ -8 \\ \hline \end{array}$$

Name _____

Put It All Together

Read the story problem. Cross out the correct number.
Then subtract to find the difference.

14  play.

7 🐕 stop.

How many 🐕
play now?

$$\begin{array}{r} 14 \\ -7 \\ \hline \end{array}$$

There are 10 🦆.

10 🦆 go away.

How many 🦆 are
left?

$$\begin{array}{r} 10 \\ -10 \\ \hline \end{array}$$

 has 3 . has 2 . How many
more does have than ?

$3-2=$ _____

 has _____ more than .

Name _____

Take a Test Drive

Fill in the bubble to show the correct answer.

$\begin{array}{r} 10 \\ -3 \\ \hline \end{array}$ ○ 7 ○ 8 ○ 9	$\begin{array}{r} 9 \\ -2 \\ \hline \end{array}$ ○ 6 ○ 7 ○ 8	$\begin{array}{r} 7 \\ -2 \\ \hline \end{array}$ ○ 4 ○ 5 ○ 6
$\begin{array}{r} 3 \\ -1 \\ \hline \end{array}$ ○ 2 ○ 3 ○ 4	$\begin{array}{r} 5 \\ -1 \\ \hline \end{array}$ ○ 4 ○ 5 ○ 6	$\begin{array}{r} 6 \\ -4 \\ \hline \end{array}$ ○ 1 ○ 2 ○ 3

Which picture matches the problem? $5 - 4 = 1$

□⊠⊠⊠⊠   □   □□□□⊠

○   ○   ○

Which problem matches the picture?

$\begin{array}{r} 5 \\ -5 \\ \hline \end{array}$ $\begin{array}{r} 10 \\ -0 \\ \hline \end{array}$ $\begin{array}{r} 10 \\ -5 \\ \hline \end{array}$ ⊠⊠⊠⊠⊠ △△△△△

○   ○   ○

Name _____

Take a Test Drive

Subtract to find the difference. Fill in the bubble beside the correct answer.

$\begin{array}{r} 5 \\ -2 \\ \hline \end{array}$ 5 ○ 3 ○ 2 ○	$\begin{array}{r} 4 \\ -3 \\ \hline \end{array}$ 7 ○ 2 ○ 1 ○
$\begin{array}{r} 8 \\ -3 \\ \hline \end{array}$ 11 ○ 6 ○ 5 ○	$\begin{array}{r} 10 \\ -6 \\ \hline \end{array}$ 8 ○ 4 ○ 3 ○
$\begin{array}{r} 18 \\ -9 \\ \hline \end{array}$ 9 ○ 8 ○ 7 ○	$\begin{array}{r} 15 \\ -7 \\ \hline \end{array}$ 11 ○ 10 ○ 8 ○
$\begin{array}{r} 20 \\ -10 \\ \hline \end{array}$ 14 ○ 11 ○ 10 ○	$\begin{array}{r} 16 \\ -5 \\ \hline \end{array}$ 11 ○ 5 ○ 1 ○

Name _____

Attributes and Location

Look at the key. Color each item.

Key

If it's round, color it blue.

If it's pointy, color it green.

If it's smooth, color it yellow.

If it's rough, color it red.

Name _____

58

Follow the directions to complete each picture.

Draw a **between** 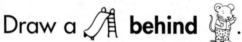 and  .

Draw a **behind** .

Draw a **in front of** .

Draw a **over** . Draw a **under** .

Advantage Math Grade 1 © 2004 Creative Teaching Press

Name _____

Recognize Shapes

Follow the directions.

The ball is a circle. Underline another circle.	
The tile is a square. Circle another square.	
The rug is a rectangle. Underline another rectangle. 	

Get Ahead

The **tri** in triangle stands for 3.

What does triangle mean? 3 angles

Circle the word part **tri** in the words below.

tricycle   trio   triplets

Name _____

Look at the key. Color each shape.

Key
circle = yellow
square = blue
rectangle = green
triangle = red

Draw a line to match the shape and the name.

triangle   □

circle   ○

square   ▭

rectangle   △

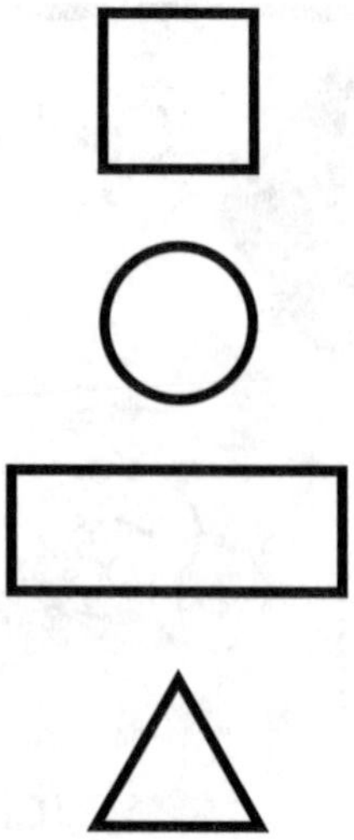

Name _____

Draw Patterns

Look at the pattern. Show what comes next.

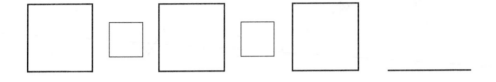

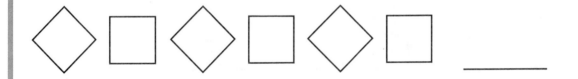

1, 2, 3, 4, 1, 2, 3, ____, 1, 2, 3, 4

Name _____

Draw Patterns

Look at the pattern. Show what comes next.

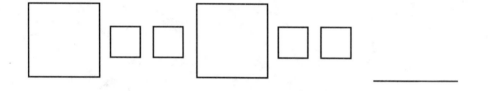

2, 4, 6, 8, 10, 12, 14, _____

Advantage Math Grade 1 © 2004 Creative Teaching Press

Name _____

Take a Test Drive

Fill in the bubble to show the correct answer.

Which shape is round?

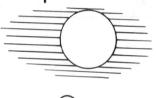   

○   ○   ○

Which animal is **behind** the  ?

○   ○   ○

Which picture shows a square **over** a square?

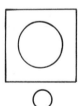   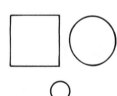

○   ○   ○

Which person is **between** and ?

○   ○   ○

Advantage Math Grade 1 © 2004 Creative Teaching Press

Name _____

Take a Test Drive

Fill in the bubble to show the correct answer.

Which shape is a circle?

○   ○   ○

Which shape is a square?

○   ○   ○

What is the name of this shape?

rectangle   triangle   square

○   ○   ○

What is the name of this shape?

rectangle   triangle   square

○   ○   ○

Which shape comes next in the pattern?

○ ○ □ △ △ ○ ○ □

□   ○   △

○   ○   ○

Advantage Math Grade 1 © 2004 Creative Teaching Press

Measurement

⭐ We measure weight with a scale. **Pounds, ounces, grams,** and **kilograms** are units of weight.

Look at each pair. Circle the object that weighs more.

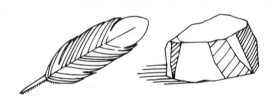

Get Ahead

Weigh yourself on a scale. Draw a line to show the item that weighs more or less than you do.

more   less

Measurement

⭐ We measure length with a ruler. **Inches, feet, yards, miles, centimeters, meters,** and **kilometers** are units of length.

Circle the picture that matches the label.

taller 	shorter 
farther  	closer 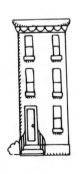
wider 	thinner 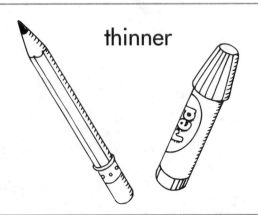

Name _____

Duration

About how long would each activity take?

walk to school

minutes   days   months

build a building

minutes   days   months

play a game

minutes   days   months

drive across the country

minutes   days   years

spend a day at school

minutes   hours   days

grow a plant

minutes   hours   days

Name _____

Time

Label each picture **before** or **after**.

 _____

 _____

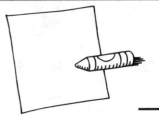 _____

 _____

 _____

Think It Through

Think about how long it takes you to complete an activity. Answer the questions.

What activity takes you minutes? _____

What activity takes you hours? _____

What activity takes you days or months?

_____

Name _____

Take a Test Drive

Fill in the bubble to show the correct answer.

Which unit is a measure of weight?	○ inch ○ hour ○ pound
Which unit is a measure of length?	○ inch ○ gram ○ hour
Which unit is a measure of time?	○ foot ○ minute ○ pound
Which is the shortest?	○ day ○ week ○ hour
Which is the longest?	○ foot ○ mile ○ inch

Take a Test Drive

Fill in the bubble under the correct answer.

Which weighs less than the ?

○   ○   ○

Which is longer than the ?

○   ○   ○

Which is shorter than the ?

○   ○   ○

Which clock shows 7:00?

○   ○   ○

Which clock shows 4:30?

○   ○   ○

Advantage Math Grade 1 © 2004 Creative Teaching Press

Name _____

Dimes

⭐ Count dimes by 10's.

1 dime is 10 cents.

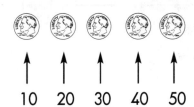

= 10¢ or $0.10

5 dimes = 50¢ or $0.50

10   20   30   40   50

Count the dimes. Count by 10 to find the amount.

   (dime) (dime) (dime) (dime)

<u>10</u>   <u>20</u>   ___   ___   ___ ¢

___ ___ ___ ___ ___ ___ ___ ___ ___   ___ ¢

Count the amount.

<u>10</u>   <u>15</u>   ___   ___   ___ ¢

___ ___ ___ ___ ___ ___ ___   ___ ¢

Advantage Math Grade 1 © 2004 Creative Teaching Press

Quarters

⭐ Count quarters by 25. 1 quarter is 25 cents.

25   50   75   100   125

= 25¢ or $0.25   = 50¢ or $0.50   5 quarters = $1.25

Count the quarters. Find the amount.

___ ___ ___   ___ ¢

___ ___ ___ ___ $ ___

Count the amount.

25 35 40 41 42 ___ ___   ___ ¢

25 50 60 65 ___ ___ ___   ___ ¢

Bills

= $1.00

= $5.00

= $10.00

Pay attention to the number on each bill!

10   15   16 $16

Count the amount.

1   2   3   4 $ __4__.00

__   __   __   __

__   __   __ $ _____.00

__   __   __   __ $ _____.00

__   __ $ _____.00

__   __   __   __   __ $ _____.00

Name _____

5
84

Bills

Count the amount.

$_____ . _____ _____

↑ dollars   ↑ cents ↑

$1.00 $1.25 $1.26 $1.26

$_____ . _____

$_____ . _____

Get Ahead

Draw lines to match the coins with their name and amount.

penny    10¢

nickel    5¢

dime   1¢

quarter   25¢

Add Money

Count the amount.

___ ___ ___ ___ ___ ___   _____ ¢

___ ___ ___ ___ ___ ___ ___ ___   _____ ¢

___ ___ ___ ___ ___ ___ ___ ___   _____ ¢

$5.00 6.00 6.25 _____ _____ $ 6.55

___ ___ ___ ___ ___ ___ ___ $ _____

Add Money

⭐ When you add money, add the one cent column first. Then add the ten cents place. Then add the dollars. Remember to write the $ and the decimal point.

	Add the cents. 2 + 0 = 2	**Add the ten cents.** 1 + 5 = 6	**Add the dollars.** 3 + 1 = 4
dollars ten cents one cents $3.12 +$1.50	dollars ten cents one cents $3.12 +1.50 $. 2	dollars ten cents one cents $3.12 +1.50 $ .62	dollars ten cents one cents $3.12 +1.50 $4.62

Add the amounts.

dollars ten cents one cents
$2.45
+$3.13

dollars ten cents one cents
$4.29
+$2.20

dollars ten cents one cents
$6.50
+$2.43

dollars ten cents one cents
$1.06
+$7.31

dollars ten cents one cents
$5.27
+$2.32

dollars ten cents one cents
$3.02
+$3.92

Name _____

Put It All Together

Count the money. Read the question. Circle the answer.

Do you have enough to buy ?

yes   no

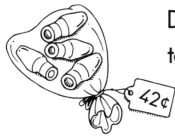

Do you have enough to buy  ?

yes   no

Do you have enough to buy  ?

yes   no

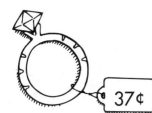

Do you have enough to buy ?

yes   no

Put It All Together

If the problem is about getting more money, add.
If it's about losing or spending money, subtract.

You have 32¢. You earn 45¢ more. How much do you have altogether?

$$\begin{array}{r} 32¢ \\ +45¢ \\ \hline ¢ \end{array}$$

You have 45¢. You spend 31¢. How much do you have left?

$$\begin{array}{r} ¢ \\ - \quad ¢ \\ \hline \end{array}$$

---

gave you 50¢. You give 30¢ back. How much do you still have?

$$\begin{array}{r} ¢ \\ - \quad ¢ \\ \hline \end{array}$$

You have 96¢. You spend 34¢. How much do you have left?

$$\begin{array}{r} ¢ \\ - \quad ¢ \\ \hline \end{array}$$

---

has 24¢. finds 63¢ more. How much does he have now?

$$\begin{array}{r} ¢ \\ + \quad ¢ \\ \hline \end{array}$$

Name _____

Take a Test Drive

Fill in the bubble beside the correct amount.

○ 3¢

○ 4¢

○ 5¢

○ 1¢

○ 10¢

○ 25¢

○ 2¢

○ 5¢

○ 10¢

○ 4¢

○ 22¢

○ 14¢

○ 3¢

○ 15¢

○ 30¢

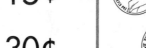

○ 50¢

○ 60¢

○ 65¢

Advantage Math Grade 1 © 2004 Creative Teaching Press

Name _____

Take a Test Drive

Fill in the bubble to show the correct answer.

How much is this?   37¢   60¢   62¢

    ○   ○   ○

How much is this?   40¢   51¢   61¢

    ○   ○   ○

How much is [ten dollar bill] worth? $10 $1 $5

    ○   ○   ○

How much is this? $6.28 $10.00 $10.28

    ○   ○   ○

How much is this? $7.36 $7.32 $1.12

$3.24
+$4.12

    ○   ○   ○

Bob has 34¢. He spends 22¢ on [gum] .

How much money is left?   46¢   22¢   12¢

    ○   ○   ○

Advantage Math Grade 1 © 2004 Creative Teaching Press

93

Graphs

★ Graphs can go up and down or side to side. Count the shapes to help fill in this bar graph.

circles ___6___   triangles _____
squares _____   stars _____

Use your numbers to help fill in the bar graph.

9				
8				
7				
6				
5				
4				
3				
2				
1				
	○	☆	△	□

Use the information on the graph to answer the questions.

Which shape do you see the least?   _____

Which shape do you see the most?   _____

How many more triangles are there than circles?   _____

How many less stars are there than squares?   _____

Name _____

Draw Graphs

Everyone had a pet to show.

John   Matt   Kate   Emma

Color the graph to show how many pets each person had.

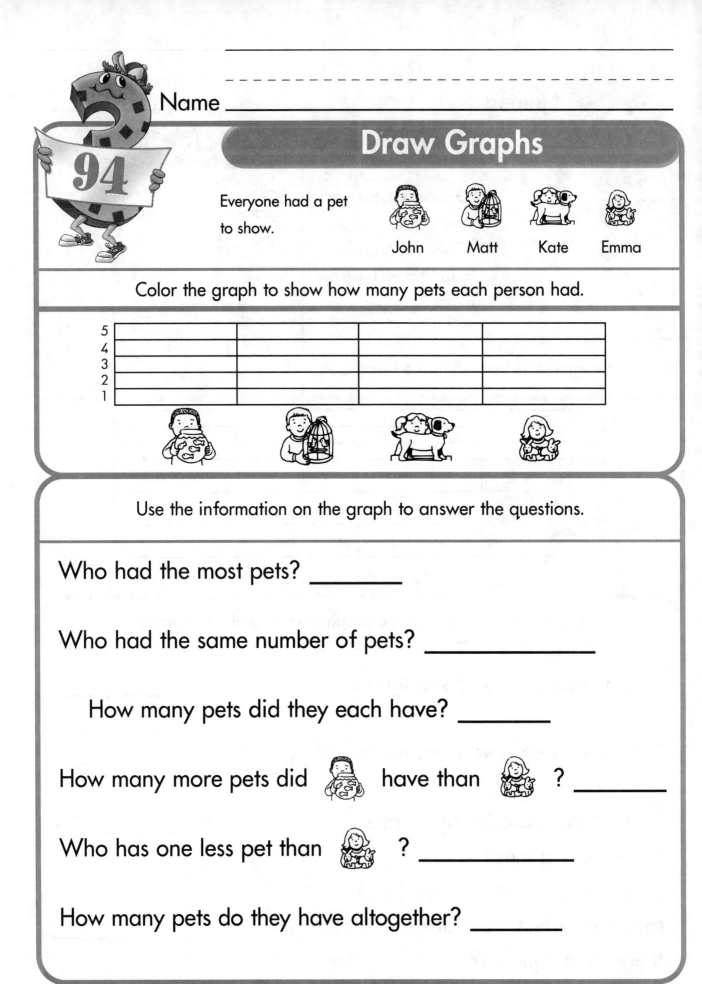

Use the information on the graph to answer the questions.

Who had the most pets? _____

Who had the same number of pets? _____

How many pets did they each have? _____

How many more pets did 🐟 have than 👧 ? _____

Who has one less pet than 🐶 ? _____

How many pets do they have altogether? _____

Name _____

Take a Test Drive

Look at the graph. Fill in the bubble to show the correct answer.

Popular Spring Sports

Baseball	⚾ ⚾ ⚾ ⚾ ⚾
Basketball	🏀 🏀 🏀
Soccer	⚽ ⚽ ⚽ ⚽
Golf	⚬

Which sport do the most people like?

Baseball	Basketball	Soccer
○	○	○

How many more people like ⚽ than ⚬ ?

2	3	4
○	○	○

What picture means 1 person likes golf?

⚬⚬⚬	⚽	⚬
○	○	○

How many people like soccer and golf?

4	5	6
○	○	○

Name _____

Take a Test Drive

Look at the graph. Fill in the bubble to show the correct answer.

Mya's Bug Collection

5				
4				
3				
2				
1				

How many 🐜 does Mya have?

    1   5   6

    ○   ○   ○

Which bug does Mya have the least of?

    ○   ○   ○

Which bug does Mya have the most of?

    ○   ○   ○

Which bug does she have one less of than 🐛 ?

    ○   ○   ○

Which bug does she have one more of than 🐞 ?

    ○   ○   ○

Advantage Math Grade 1 © 2004 Creative Teaching Press

Name _____

Posttest

Fill in the bubble beside the correct answer.

Which number is five?	○ 4
	○ 5
	○ 8

Which word means 7?	○ four
	○ six
	○ seven

How many 🐸 are there?	○ 6
	○ 8
	○ 9

Which tells where 🐕 is?	○ first
	○ second
	○ third

Which number comes after 19?	○ 20
	○ 21
	○ 191

Name _____

Fill in the bubble beside the correct answer.

Which number comes after 37?	○ 36 ○ 38 ○ 40
Which number comes before 81?	○ 79 ○ 80 ○ 82
How many tens and ones are in the number 14?	○ 14 ones ○ 1 ten 4 ones ○ 10 tens 4 ones
8 + 7 =	○ 13 ○ 15 ○ 87
9 − 5 ___	○ 3 ○ 4 ○ 9

Name _____

Posttest

Fill in the bubble beside the correct answer.

$3+2+2=$

- ○ 3
- ○ 7
- ○ 32

$12+7=$

- ○ 19
- ○ 21
- ○ 27

$\begin{array}{r} 5 \\ +8 \\ \hline \end{array}$

- ○ 11
- ○ 13
- ○ 15

$\begin{array}{r} 16 \\ +4 \\ \hline \end{array}$

- ○ 18
- ○ 20
- ○ 22

There are 3 🐞.
1 more 🐞 comes.
How many 🐞
are there in all?

- ○ 2
- ○ 3
- ○ 4

$9-3=$

- ○ 3
- ○ 6
- ○ 12

Name _____

Posttest

Fill in the bubble below the correct answer.

What is this shape?

circle   square   triangle

◯   ◯   ◯

What number comes next in the pattern?

3, 6, 9, 12, 15, _____

16   18   20

◯   ◯   ◯

What time is it?

1:00   10:00   11:00

◯   ◯   ◯

Which clock shows 2:30?

◯   ◯   ◯

Look at the graph. Fill in the bubble to show the correct answer.

1¢	● ● ●
5¢	● ● ●
10¢	● ● ● ●
25¢	●

How much is the row of dimes worth?

10¢   30¢   40¢

◯   ◯   ◯

What is the amount of money altogether?

11¢   83¢   88¢

◯   ◯   ◯

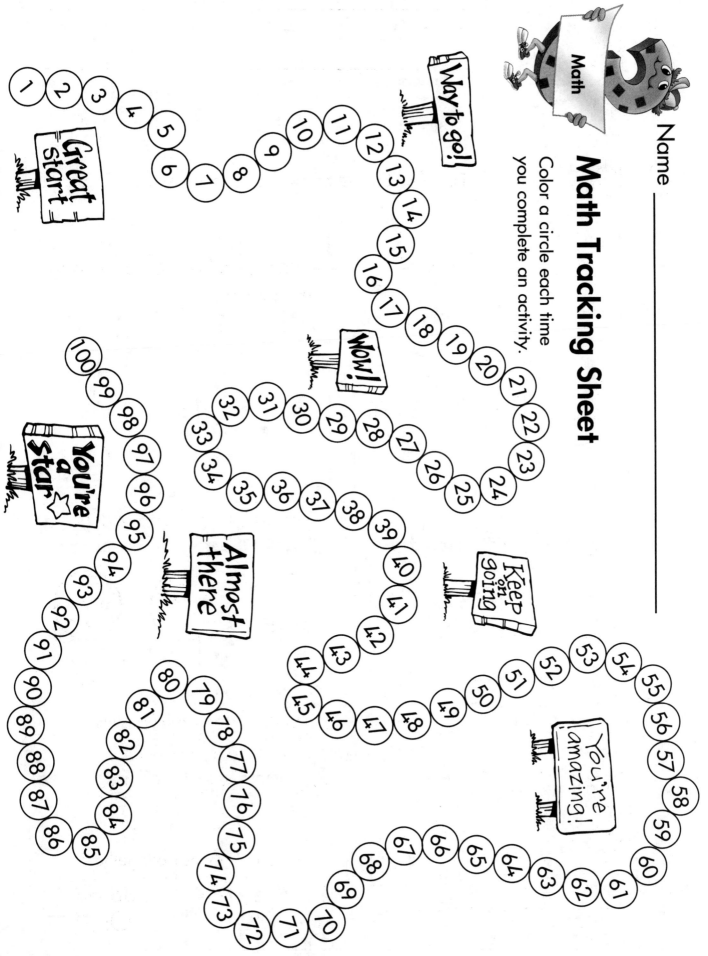

Name _____

Math Tracking Sheet

Color a circle each time
you complete an activity.

Great Start

Way to go!

Wow!

Keep on going

You're amazing!

Almost there

You're a Star

Answer Key

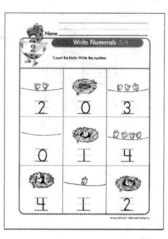

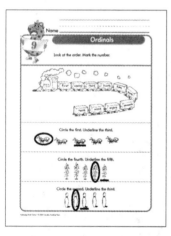

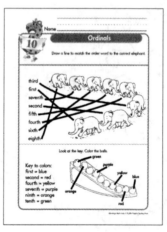

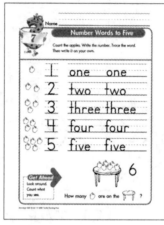

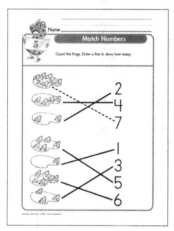

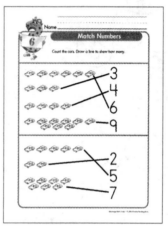

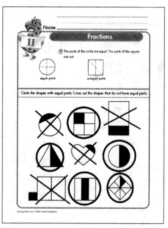

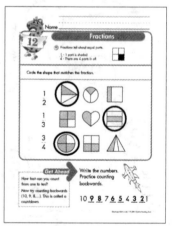

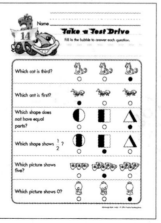

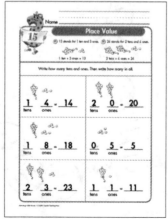

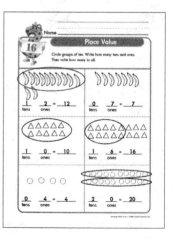

17 — Count to Twenty
What comes after the number 10? Write each number.

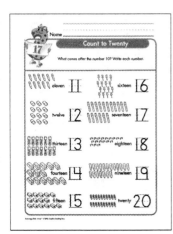

eleven 11   sixteen 16
twelve 12   seventeen 17
thirteen 13   eighteen 18
fourteen 14   nineteen 19
fifteen 15   twenty 20

18 — Count to Twenty
Draw a line to match the picture, number, and word.

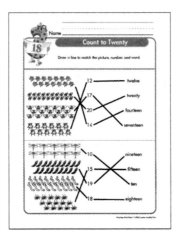

12 — twelve
17 — twenty
20 — fourteen
14 — seventeen

10 — nineteen
15 — fifteen
19 — ten
18 — eighteen

19 — Count to One Hundred
Count the tens and ones. Write how many tens and ones. Then write how many in all.

4 tens 0 ones = 40
7 tens 1 ones = 71
1 tens 3 ones = 13
1 tens 8 ones = 18
3 tens 5 ones = 35
0 tens 9 ones = 9

20 — Count to One Hundred
Follow the pattern to complete the chart.

1	2	3	4	5	6	7	8	9	10
11	12	13	14	15	16	17	18	19	20
21	22	23	24	25	26	27	28	29	30
31	32	33	34	35	36	37	38	39	40
41	42	43	44	45	46	47	48	49	50
51	52	53	54	55	56	57	58	59	60
61	62	63	64	65	66	67	68	69	70
71	72	73	74	75	76	77	78	79	80
81	82	83	84	85	86	87	88	89	90
91	92	93	94	95	96	97	98	99	100

21 — Order Numbers
Write the number that comes next.

12, 13, 14, **15**   23, 24, 25, **26**
79, 80, 81, **82**   45, 46, 47, **48**
37, 38, 39, **40**   88, 89, 90, **91**
64, 65, 66, **67**   97, 98, 99, **100**
8, 9, 10, **11**   56, 57, 58, **59**
30, 31, 32, **33**   41, 42, 43, **44**

22 — Order Numbers
Write the number that comes before.

21 22   **56** 57   **8** 9
73 74   **80** 81   **39** 40
48 49   **59** 60   **37** 38
32 33   **64** 65   **25** 26

Think It Through
1. The red crayon is to the left of the yellow crayon.
2. Neither the blue crayon nor the red crayon is in the middle.
Which is first? Which is second? Which is third? The crayons are red, blue, and yellow. Use the clues to color the crayons the correct color.
red   yellow   blue

23 — Skip Counting
It's fun to make a pattern by skip counting.

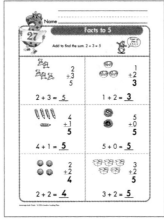

Show how the frog counts by 2's all the way to 12.
Show how the frog counts by 3's all the way to 12.
Show how the frog counts by 4's all the way to 12.
Show how the frog counts by 5's all the way to 15.

24 — Skip Counting
Count the legs. Write how many on each line.

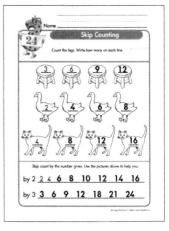

3 6 9 12
2 4 6 8
4 8 12 16

Skip count by the number given. Use the pictures above to help you.
by 2 2 4 6 8 10 12 14 16
by 3 3 6 9 12 18 21 24

25 — Take a Test Drive
Look at the number. Fill in the bubble under the picture that matches.

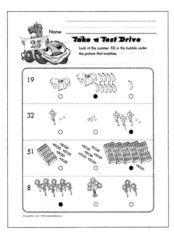

19
32
51
8

26 — Take a Test Drive
Fill in the bubble under the correct answer.

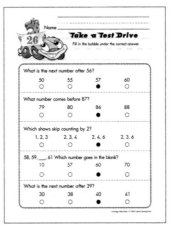

What is the next number after 56?
50   55   57   60

What number comes before 87?
79   80   86   88

Which shows skip counting by 2?
1, 2, 3   2, 3, 4   2, 4, 6   2, 3, 6

58, 59, ___, 61 Which number goes in the blank?
10   57   60   70

What is the next number after 39?
30   38   40   41

27 — Facts to 5
Add to find the sum. 2 + 3 = 5

2
+3
5

1
+2
3

2 + 3 = 5   1 + 2 = 3

4
+1
5

5
+0
5

4 + 1 = 5   5 + 0 = 5

2
+2
4

3
+2
5

2 + 2 = 4   3 + 2 = 5

28 — Facts to 5
Complete the picture. Add to find the sum.

0
+3
3

4
+1
5

0 + 3 = 3   4 + 1 = 5

1
+3
4

4
+3
7

1 + 3 = 4   4 + 3 = 7

2
+1
3

1
+4
5

2 + 1 = 3   1 + 4 = 5

29 — Facts to 5
Draw a picture to illustrate the problem. Add to find the sum.

3
+1
4

2
+0
2

2
+2
4

4
+1
5

0 + 3 = 3   3 + 2 = 5
1 + 2 = 3   4 + 0 = 4

30 — Facts to 5
Add to find the sum.

2   3   4   3
+1   +2   +0   +1
3   5   4   4

1   0   2   0
+3   +5   +2   +3
4   5   4   3

0 + 0 = 0   1 + 2 = 3   2 + 3 = 5
4 + 1 = 5   1 + 1 = 2   3 + 1 = 4

31 — Facts to 10
Complete the picture. Add to find the sum.

6   3   2
+2   +4   +5
8   7   7

6   3   8
+4   +7   +0
10   10   8

Think It Through
Count on to find the missing number.
1 + 3 = 4
4 + 2 = 6
5 + 5 = 10

32 — Facts to 10
Add to find the sum.

4   2   4   2
+1   +5   +4   +7
5   7   8   9

8   6   3   10
+2   +4   +3   +0
10   10   6   10

5 + 1 = 6   4 + 3 = 7   3 + 6 = 9
8 + 2 = 10   0 + 7 = 7   5 + 5 = 10

33 — Addition to Twenty

Complete the picture. Add to find the sum.

$8+3=11$ $2+10=12$
$7+6=13$ $9+4=13$
$5+8=13$ $10+10=20$
$7+7=14$ $7+8=15$

34 — Addition to Twenty

Add to find the sum.

$7+5=12$ $20+0=20$ $8+7=15$ $8+4=12$
$9+8=17$ $7+8=15$ $8+6=14$ $9+5=14$
$1+10=11$ $5+6=11$ $9+1=11$ $10+6=16$

$4+7=11$ $10+5=15$ $8+8=16$

35 — Add 3 Numbers

Draw the picture. Add to find the sum.

$3+2+1=6$ $1+2+1=4$
$6+3+0=9$ $2+4+1=7$

$5+1+2=8$ $3+4+2=9$
$4+5+1=10$ $2+0+7=9$

36 — Add 3 Numbers

Add to find the sum.

$0+2+1=3$ $3+5+1=9$ $4+2+2=8$ $6+4+5=15$
$6+2+3=11$ $8+0+1=9$ $5+4+3=12$ $7+6+3=16$
$1+7+4=12$ $2+0+6=8$ $3+9+2=14$ $5+3+6=14$

$4+3+2=9$ $5+1+7=13$

37 — Add 1-Digit and 2-Digit Numbers

Complete the picture. Add to find the sum.

$1+10=11$ $11+3=14$
$4+14=18$ $9+7=16$
$15+5=20$ $6+10=16$
$12+6=18$ $10+8=18$

38 — Add 1-Digit and 2-Digit Numbers

Add to find the sum.

$12+5=17$ $16+2=18$ $13+4=17$ $11+6=17$
$19+1=20$ $7+13=20$ $5+12=17$ $14+4=18$
$15+3=18$ $0+20=20$ $11+8=19$ $17+3=20$
$16+4=20$ $2+14=16$ $7+10=17$ $18+1=19$

39 — Put It All Together

Read the story problem. Write the number sentence. Then add to find the answer.

3 sit on a log. 2 more hop on. How many are there in all? $3+2=5$

4 eat. 1 more eats. How many eat in all? $4+1=5$

3 swim. 3 more swim. How many swim in all? $3+3=6$

5 swim. 2 more swim. How many swim in all? $5+2=7$

40 — Put It All Together

Read the story problem. Write the number sentence. Then add to find the answer.

6 float. 2 more float. How many float in all? $6+2=8$

There are 2. 2 more come. How many are there in all? $2+2=4$

There are 5. 2 more come. How many are there in all? $5+2=7$

There are 3. 4 more come. How many are there in all? $3+4=7$

41 — Take a Test Drive

Fill in the bubble to show the correct answer.

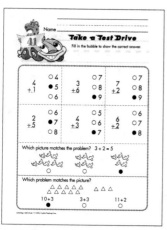

$4+1$: ○4 ●5 ○6
$3+6$: ○7 ○8 ●9
$7+2$: ○7 ○8 ●9
$2+5$: ○6 ●7 ○8
$4+3$: ○5 ○6 ●7
$6+2$: ○6 ○7 ●8

Which picture matches the problem? $3+2=5$

Which problem matches the picture?
$10+3$ $3+3$ $11+2$ → $10+3$

42 — Take a Test Drive

Fill in the bubble beside the correct answer.

$7+7$: ●14 ○15 ○16
$12+2$: ○13 ●14 ○15
$9+7$: ○11 ●16 ○17
$5+8$: ○11 ○12 ●13
$12+6$: ○14 ●18 ○19
$5+15$: ○10 ○18 ●20
$3+2$: ●5 ○6 ○7
$1+5$: ○5 ●6 ○8

43 — Facts to 5

Subtract to find the difference.

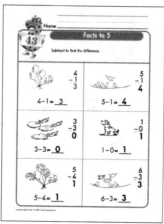

$4-1=3$ $5-1=4$
$3-3=0$ $1-0=1$
$5-4=1$ $6-3=3$

44 — Facts to 5

Subtract to find the difference.

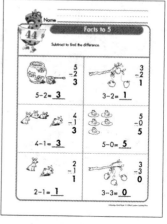

$5-2=3$ $3-2=1$
$4-1=3$ $5-0=5$
$2-1=1$ $3-3=0$

45 — Facts to 5

Cross out shapes to show the number being subtracted. Subtract to find the difference.

$2-1=1$ $4-2=2$
$3-2=1$ $5-5=0$
$4-3=1$ $3-1=2$

46 — Facts to 5

Cross out shapes to show the number being subtracted. Subtract to find the difference.

$4-2=2$ $2-1=1$
$5-4=1$ $3-3=0$
$4-0=0$ $5-2=3$

47 — Facts to 10

Cross out shapes to show the number being subtracted. Subtract to find the difference.

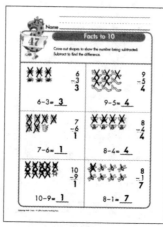

$6-3=3$ $9-5=4$
$7-6=1$ $8-4=4$
$10-9=1$ $8-1=7$

48 — Facts to 10

Draw the picture. Cross out the correct number. Subtract to find the difference.

$7-3=4$ $10-5=5$ $8-5=3$
$9-8=1$ $9-4=5$ $6-3=3$

Think It Through
Find the missing number.

$5-\boxed{2}=3$
$6-\boxed{4}=2$
$10-\boxed{3}=7$

How did you find the missing number?

49 — Subtracting from 20 and Below

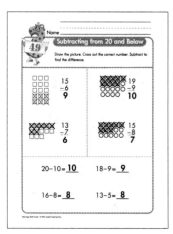

Draw the picture. Cross out the correct number. Subtract to find the difference.

$15 - 6 = 9$ $19 - 9 = 10$

$13 - 7 = 6$ $15 - 8 = 7$

$20 - 10 = \underline{10}$ $18 - 9 = \underline{9}$

$16 - 8 = \underline{8}$ $13 - 5 = \underline{8}$

50 — Subtracting from 20 and Below

Draw the picture. Cross out the correct number. Subtract to find the difference.

$18 - 3 = 15$ $16 - 4 = 12$

$14 - 2 = 12$ $19 - 9 = 10$

$17 - 3 = 14$ $12 - 5 = 7$

$20 - 6 = \underline{14}$ $15 - 4 = \underline{11}$

51 — Subtracting from 20 and Below

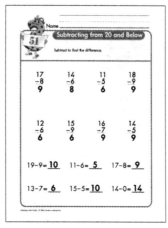

Subtract to find the difference.

$17 - 8 = 9$ $14 - 6 = 8$ $11 - 6 = 5$ $18 - 9 = 9$

$12 - 6 = 6$ $15 - 9 = 6$ $16 - 7 = 9$ $14 - 5 = 9$

$19 - 9 = \underline{10}$ $11 - 6 = \underline{5}$ $17 - 8 = \underline{9}$

$13 - 7 = \underline{6}$ $15 - 5 = \underline{10}$ $14 - 0 = \underline{14}$

52 — Subtracting from 20 and Below

Subtract to find the difference.

$18 - 9 = 9$ $16 - 5 = 11$ $13 - 7 = 6$ $10 - 7 = 3$

$17 - 3 = 14$ $12 - 6 = 6$ $15 - 8 = 7$ $14 - 6 = 8$

Get Ahead
Read the story problem. Subtract to find the difference. Add to find the sum. Hint: A drawing may help you find the answer.

Ben had 12. He gave 4 to his friend Matt. On his birthday, Ben got 2 new. How many does Ben have now? __10__

53 — Put It All Together

Read the story problem. Then read the question. Cross out the correct number. Then subtract to find the difference.

4 eat. 2 fly away. How many are left? $4 - 2 = 2$

9 swim. 5 swim away. How many are left? $9 - 5 = 4$

7 sit. 1 hops away. How many are left? $7 - 1 = 6$

12 dig. 8 stop. How many dig now? $12 - 8 = 4$

54 — Put It All Together

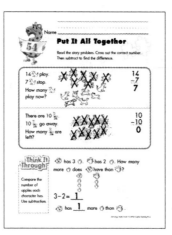

Read the story problem. Cross out the correct number. Then subtract to find the difference.

14 play. 7 stop. How many play now? $14 - 7 = 7$

There are 10. 10 go away. How many are left? $10 - 10 = 0$

Think It Through
Compare the number of apples each character has. Use subtraction.
has 3. has 2. How many more does have than? $3 - 2 = \underline{1}$
has __1__ more than.

55 — Take a Test Drive

Fill in the bubble to show the correct answer.

$10 - 3$: 7, ●8, 9
$9 - 2$: 6, ●7, 8
$7 - 2$: ●4, 5, 6

$3 - 1$: ●2, 3, 4
$5 - 1$: ●4, 5, 6
$6 - 4$: 1, ●2, 3

Which picture matches the problem? $5 - 4 = 1$

Which problem matches the picture?

56 — Take a Test Drive

Subtract to find the difference. Fill in the bubble beside the correct answer.

$5 - 2$: 5, ●3, 2
$4 - 3$: 7, 2, ●1

$8 - 3$: 11, 6, ●5
$10 - 6$: 8, ●4, 3

$18 - 9$: ●9, 8, 7
$15 - 7$: 11, 10, ●8

$20 - 10$: 14, ●11, 10
$16 - 5$: ●11, 5, 1

57 — Attributes and Location

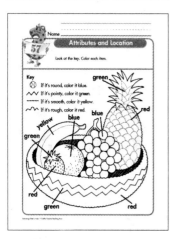

Look at the key. Color each item.

Key
If it's round, color it blue.
If it's pointy, color it green.
If it's smooth, color it yellow.
If it's rough, color it red.

58 — Attributes and Location

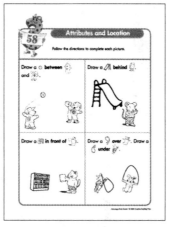

Follow the directions to complete each picture.

Draw a between and. Draw a behind.

Draw a in front of. Draw a over. Draw a under.

59 — Recognize Shapes

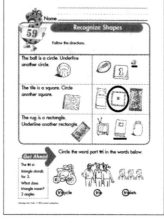

Follow the directions.

The ball is a circle. Underline another circle.

The tile is a square. Circle another square.

The rug is a rectangle. Underline another rectangle.

Get Ahead
The tri in triangle stands for 3. What does triangle mean? 3 angles.

Circle the word part tri in the words below.
tricycle trio triplets

60 — Recognize Shapes

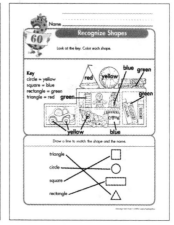

Look at the key. Color each shape.

Key
circle = yellow
square = blue
rectangle = green
triangle = red

Draw a line to match the shape and the name.
triangle
circle
square
rectangle

61 — Draw Shapes

Follow the directions to complete each picture.

Draw a circle. Draw a square.

Draw a rectangle. Draw a triangle.

62 — Draw Shapes

Follow the directions to create a picture.

1. Draw a large square.
2. Draw a large triangle on top of the square.
3. Go to the bottom of the square. Draw a tall rectangle within the square, starting at the bottom.
4. Draw a small circle over the rectangle.
5. Did you draw a house? Finish your drawing.

63 — Draw Patterns

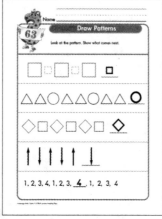

Look at the pattern. Show what comes next.

$1, 2, 3, 4, 1, 2, 3, \underline{4}, 1, 2, 3, 4$

64 — Draw Patterns

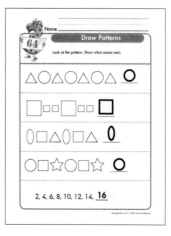

Look at the pattern. Show what comes next.

$2, 4, 6, 8, 10, 12, 14, \underline{16}$

65 Take a Test Drive
Fill in the bubble to show the correct answer.

Which shape is round?

Which animal is **behind** the cat?

Which picture shows a square **over** a square?

Which person is **between** them?

66 Take a Test Drive
Fill in the bubble to show the correct answer.

Which shape is a circle?

Which shape is a square?

What is the name of this shape? rectangle / triangle / square

What is the name of this shape? rectangle / triangle / square

Which shape comes next in the pattern?

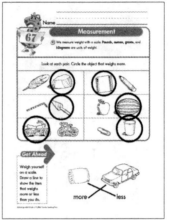

67 Measurement
We measure weight with a scale. Pounds, ounces, grams, and kilograms are units of weight.

Look at each pair. Circle the object that weighs more.

Get Ahead
Weigh yourself on a scale. Draw a line to show the items that weighs more or less than you do.

more — less

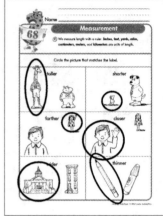

68 Measurement
We measure length with a ruler. Inches, feet, yards, miles, centimeters, meters, and kilometers are units of length.

Circle the picture that matches the label.

taller / shorter

farther / closer

thinner

69 Measuring Length with a Ruler
Circle the objects that are about 1 inch long.

Draw another object that is about 1 inch long.

Answers will vary.

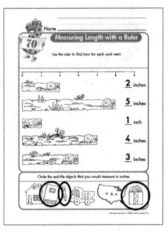

70 Measuring Length with a Ruler
Use the ruler to find how far each snail went.

2 inches
5 inches
1 inch
4 inches
3 inches

Circle the real-life objects that you would measure in inches.

71 Time to the Hour
The little hand points to the hour. The big hand points to the minute. When the big hand points to 12, look at the little hand to tell the hour.

3 o'clock 3:00

Circle the correct time.

12:00 / 1:00 / 2:00   7:00 / 8:00 / 12:00
12:00 / 11:00 / 1:00   4:00 / 5:00 / 12:00

Write the time the clock shows.

1:00   5:00
9:00   12:00

72 Time to the Hour
Draw the hour hand to show the time.

2:00   6:00
10:00   7:00

Draw the hour hand and the minute hand to show the time.

1:00   8:00
11:00   3:00

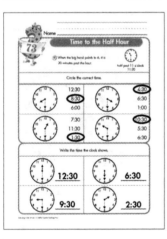

73 Time to the Half Hour
When the big hand points to 6, it is 30 minutes past the hour.

half past 11 o'clock 11:30

Circle the correct time.

12:30 / 8:30 / 6:00   4:30 / 1:00
7:30 / 11:30 / 1:30   10:30 / 5:30 / 6:30

Write the time the clock shows.

12:30   6:30
9:30   2:30

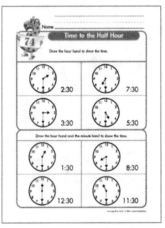

74 Time to the Half Hour
Draw the hour hand to show the time.

2:30   7:30
3:30   5:30

Draw the hour hand and the minute hand to show the time.

1:30   8:30
12:30   11:30

75 Duration
About how long would each activity take?

walk to school — minutes / days / months
build a building — minutes / days / months
play a game — minutes / days / months
drive across the country — minutes / days / years
spend a day at school — minutes / hours / days
grow a plant — minutes / hours / days

Think It Through
Think about how long it takes you to complete an activity. Answer the questions.

What activity takes you minutes? ___
What activity takes you hours? ___
What activity takes you days or months? ___

76 Time
Label each picture **before** or **after**.

before   after
after   before
before   after

Answers will vary.

77 Take a Test Drive
Fill in the bubble to show the correct answer.

Which unit is a measure of weight?
○ inch ○ hour ● pound

Which unit is a measure of length?
● inch ○ gram ○ hour

Which unit is a measure of time?
○ foot ● minute ○ pound

Which is the shortest?
○ day ○ week ● hour

Which is the longest?
○ foot ● mile ○ inch

78 Take a Test Drive
Fill in the bubble under the correct answer.

Which weighs less than the rabbit?

Which is longer than the turtle?

Which is shorter than the tree?

Which clock shows 7:00?

Which clock shows 4:30?

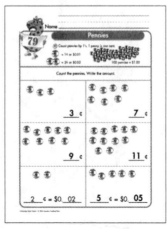

79 Pennies
Count pennies by 1's. 1 penny is one cent.
1¢ = $0.01
2¢ = $0.02
100 pennies = $1.00

Count the pennies. Write the amount.

3¢   7¢
9¢   11¢
2¢ = $0.02   5¢ = $0.05

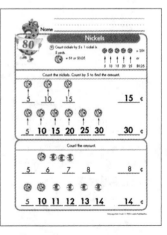

80 Nickels
Count nickels by 5's. 1 nickel is 5 cents.
5¢ = $0.05
5 10 15 20 25 = $0.25

Count the nickels. Count by 5 to find the amount.

5 10 15   15¢
5 10 15 20 25 30   30¢

Count the amount.

5 6 7 8   8¢
5 10 11 12 13 14   14¢

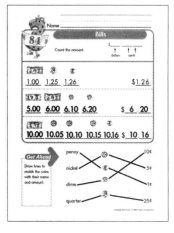

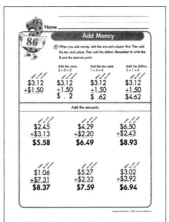

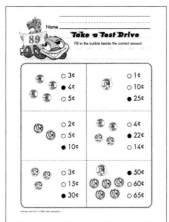

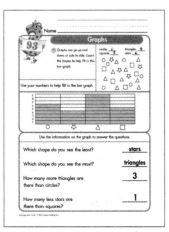

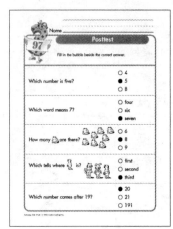

97 — Posttest

Fill in the bubble beside the correct answer.

Which number is five?
- ○ 4
- ● 5
- ○ 8

Which word means 7?
- ○ four
- ○ six
- ● seven

How many are there?
- ● 6
- ○ 8
- ○ 9

Which tells where is?
- ○ first
- ○ second
- ● third

Which number comes after 19?
- ● 20
- ○ 21
- ○ 191

98 — Posttest

Fill in the bubble beside the correct answer.

Which number comes after 37?
- ○ 36
- ● 38
- ○ 40

Which number comes before 81?
- ○ 79
- ● 80
- ○ 82

How many tens and ones are in the number 14?
- ○ 14 ones
- ● 1 ten 4 ones
- ○ 10 tens 4 ones

$8 + 7 =$
- ○ 13
- ● 15
- ○ 87

$\begin{array}{r} 9 \\ -\ 5 \\ \hline \end{array}$
- ○ 3
- ● 4
- ○ 9

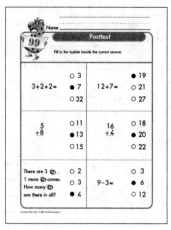

99 — Posttest

Fill in the bubble beside the correct answer.

$3+2+2 =$
- ○ 3
- ● 7
- ○ 32

$12 + 7 =$
- ● 19
- ○ 21
- ○ 27

$\begin{array}{r} 5 \\ +8 \\ \hline \end{array}$
- ○ 11
- ● 13
- ○ 15

$\begin{array}{r} 16 \\ +4 \\ \hline \end{array}$
- ○ 18
- ● 20
- ○ 22

There are 3 . 1 more comes. How many are there in all?
- ○ 2
- ○ 3
- ● 4

$9 - 3 =$
- ○ 3
- ● 6
- ○ 12

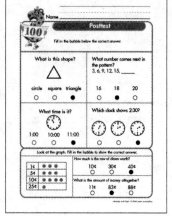

100 — Posttest

Fill in the bubble below the correct answer.

What is this shape?

circle square triangle
- ○ ○ ●

What number comes next in the pattern?
3, 6, 9, 12, 15, _____

16   18   20
- ○   ○   ●

What time is it?

1:00   10:00   11:00
- ○   ●   ○

Which clock shows 2:30?
- ○   ●   ○

Look at the graph. Fill in the bubble to show the correct answer.

1¢	● ● ●
5¢	● ● ●
10¢	● ● ●
25¢	● ●

How much is the row of dimes worth?

10¢   30¢   40¢
- ○   ●   ○

What is the amount of money altogether?

11¢   83¢   88¢
- ○   ○   ●